# BIG CHART HITS

**WISE PUBLICATIONS**
PART OF THE MUSIC SALES GROUP
LONDON / NEW YORK / PARIS / SYDNEY / COPENHAGEN / BERLIN / MADRID / HONG KONG / TOKYO

PUBLISHED BY
**WISE PUBLICATIONS**
14-15 BERNERS STREET, LONDON, W1T 3LJ, UK.

EXCLUSIVE DISTRIBUTORS:
**MUSIC SALES LIMITED**
DISTRIBUTION CENTRE, NEWMARKET ROAD, BURY ST EDMUNDS,
SUFFOLK, IP33 3YB, UK.
**MUSIC SALES PTY LIMITED**
20 RESOLUTION DRIVE, CARINGBAH, NSW 2229, AUSTRALIA.

ORDER NO. AM1004839
ISBN 978-1-78038-578-5
THIS BOOK © COPYRIGHT 2012 BY WISE PUBLICATIONS,
A DIVISION OF MUSIC SALES LIMITED.

MUSIC ARRANGED BY ZOE BOLTON.
EDITED BY JENNI NOREY.
PRINTED IN THE EU.

YOUR GUARANTEE OF QUALITY
AS PUBLISHERS, WE STRIVE TO PRODUCE EVERY BOOK TO THE HIGHEST
COMMERCIAL STANDARDS. THE MUSIC HAS BEEN FRESHLY ENGRAVED AND
THE BOOK HAS BEEN CAREFULLY DESIGNED TO MINIMISE AWKWARD PAGE
TURNS AND TO MAKE PLAYING FROM IT A REAL PLEASURE.
PARTICULAR CARE HAS BEEN GIVEN TO SPECIFYING ACID-FREE, NEUTRAL-
SIZED PAPER MADE FROM PULPS WHICH HAVE NOT BEEN ELEMENTAL
CHLORINE BLEACHED. THIS PULP IS FROM FARMED SUSTAINABLE FORESTS
AND WAS PRODUCED WITH SPECIAL REGARD FOR THE ENVIRONMENT.
THROUGHOUT, THE PRINTING AND BINDING HAVE BEEN PLANNED TO
ENSURE A STURDY, ATTRACTIVE PUBLICATION WHICH SHOULD GIVE YEARS
OF ENJOYMENT. IF YOUR COPY FAILS TO MEET OUR HIGH STANDARDS,
PLEASE INFORM US AND WE WILL GLADLY REPLACE IT.

WWW.MUSICSALES.COM

# BIG CHART HITS

# The A Team

**Words & Music by Ed Sheeran**

After meeting a girl called Angel when he played a Christmas gig for the homeless charity Crisis, singer-song-writer Ed Sheeran was inspired to write this song, based on her story. Released as the lead single from his first album, it entered the charts at No. 3, becoming the highest-selling debut UK single in the first half of 2011.

**Hints & Tips:** The rhythm of the melody is quite tricky in places. Play through the right hand a few times before putting it together with the left, making sure you're confident with the timing.

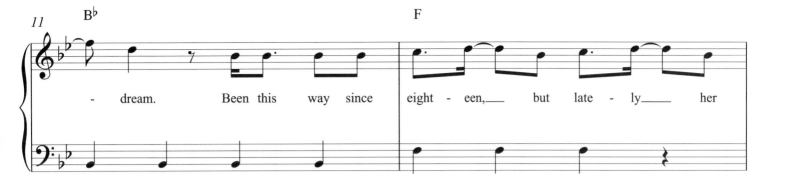

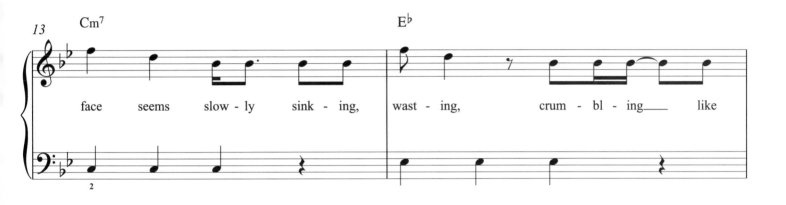

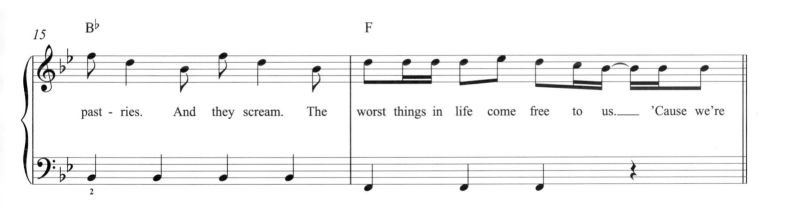

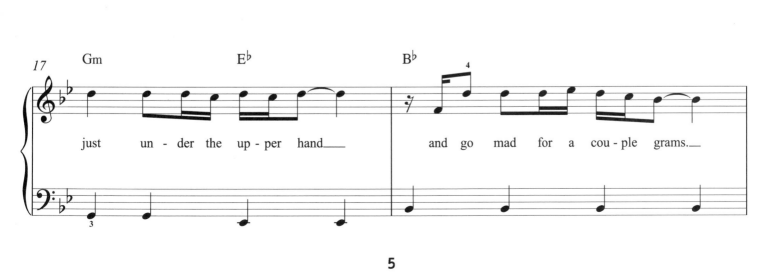

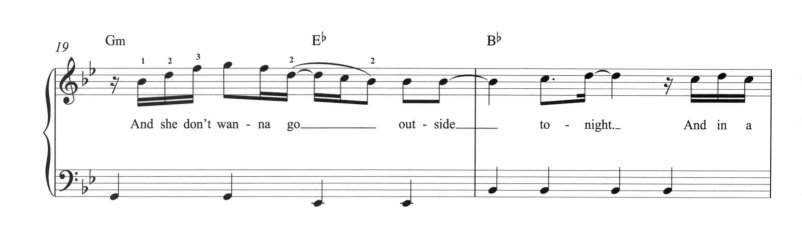

And she don't wan - na go_____ out - side_____ to - night._ And in a

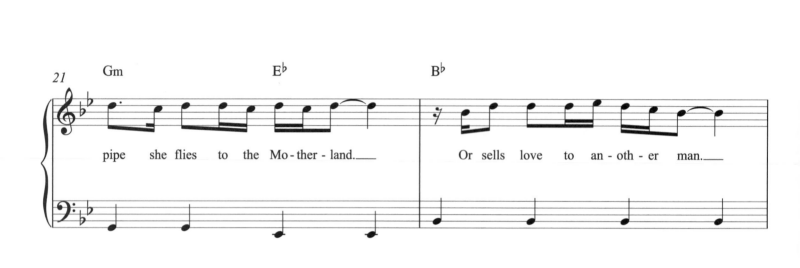

pipe she flies to the Mo - ther - land._____ Or sells love to an - oth - er man._____

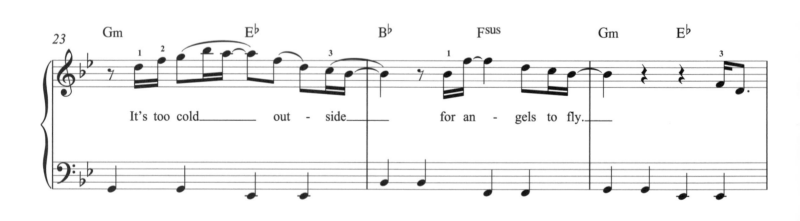

It's too cold_____ out - side_____ for an - gels to fly._____

For an - gels to fly._____

# All About Tonight

**Words & Music by Brian Kidd, Thomas James & Tebey Ottoh**

This up-tempo pop song, included on Pixie Lott's second album *Young Foolish Happy*, was intended to achieve a breakthrough for her in America, but shot straight to the top of the UK Singles Chart on its digital release in September 2011, making it her third UK No. 1. She also performed it at the 2011 Royal Variety Performance.

**Hints & Tips:** Keep the repeated quavers in the right hand melody (from bar 24) steady and even; try alternating your fingers on each note to stop it sounding too sluggish.

show all the boys___ what I got._____ I'm let-ting go of the hurt

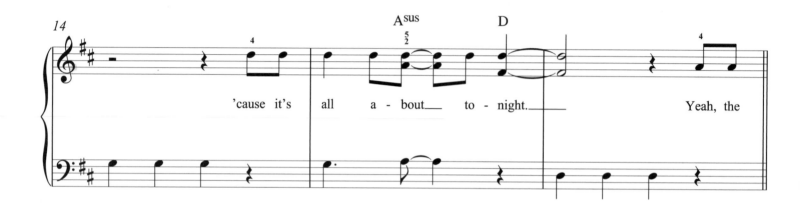

'cause it's all a-bout___ to-night.___ Yeah, the

night is a-live, you can feel the heart-beat. Let's just go with the flow, we've been

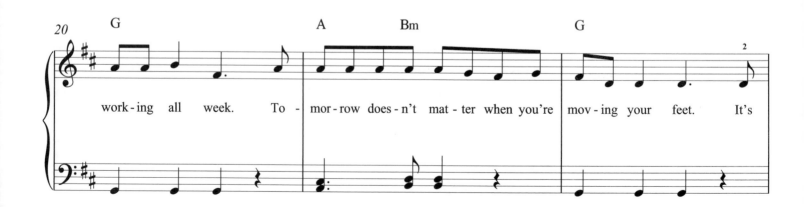

work-ing all week. To-mor-row does-n't mat-ter when you're mov-ing your feet. It's

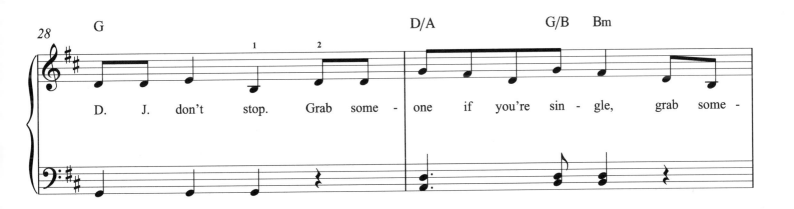

# Dance With Me Tonight

**Words & Music by Stephen Robson, Claude Kelly & Olly Murs**

Reminiscent of the '60s, with its hip-shaking bass line and effervescent horn section, this was the second single to be taken from the former X Factor contestant's second album *In Case You Didn't Know*. After being held up at No. 2 for a couple of weeks, it overtook the programme's 2011 charity release to become his third UK No. 1.

**Hints & Tips:** In this bouncy, up-beat song, remember to give the quavers that 'swing' feel. In bars 17 and 18, make sure you keep the right hand F held down while you play the notes above.

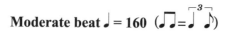

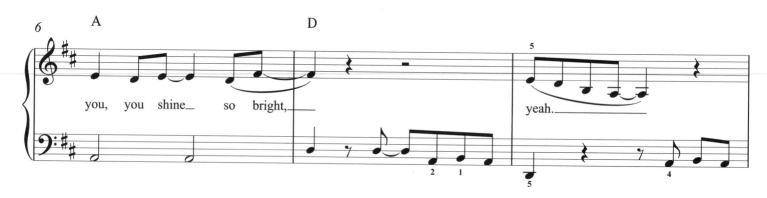

# Heaven

**Words & Music by Emeli Sandé, Mike Spencer, Harry Craze,
Shahid Khan & Hugo Chegwin**

Having written and recorded several Top 10 hits with other artists this Scottish soul singer only entered the music business full-time after completing her medical studies at the University of Glasgow. Named as the Brit Awards Critics' Choice for 2012, this song about clubbing was her debut solo single, released in August 2011.

**Hints & Tips:** Practise each hand separately until you've got the hang of the tricky rhythms before trying them together.

# I Won't Let You Go

### Words & Music by Martin Brammer, Steve Robson
### & James Morrison

The first release from Morrison's third album *The Awakening*, this passionate ballad about his long-term girlfriend and mother of his daughter follows the same heartfelt acoustic template as his previous two singles. Debuting at No. 5 in the UK, it was a success throughout Europe.

**Hints & Tips:** Play this song with feeling, bringing out the melody. When you get to the chorus, try playing it *forte*, but keep the repeated notes (bars 17 and 18) light, otherwise they will sound too heavy.

**Moderate ballad tempo**

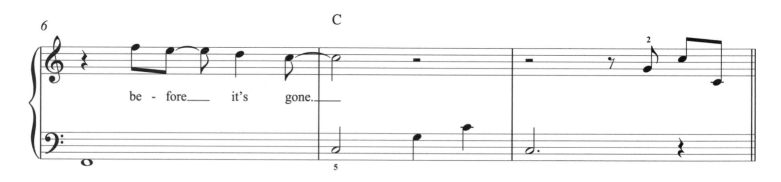

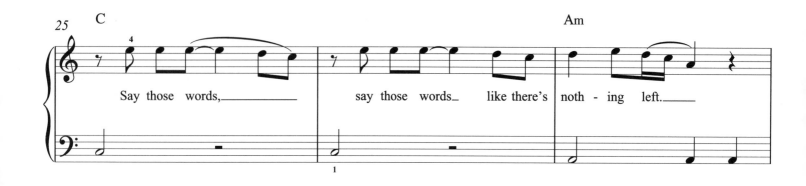

Say those words,_____ say those words__ like there's noth - ing left._____

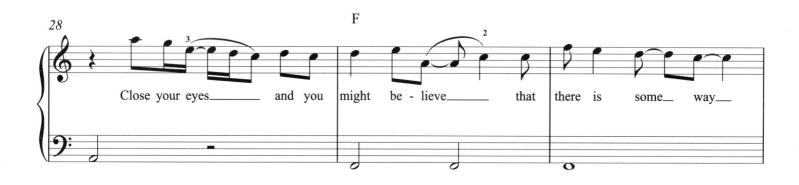

Close your eyes_____ and you might be - lieve_____ that there is some__ way__

out. O - pen up,_____ o - pen up your__

heart to__ me now.__ Let it all__ come pour - ing out._____ There's

*D.S. al Fine*

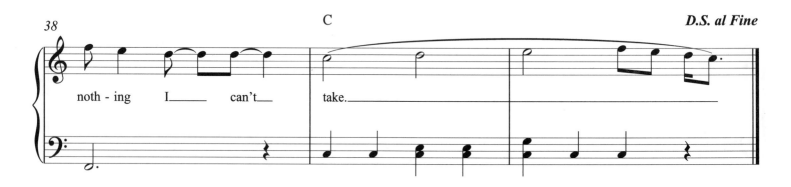

noth - ing I__ can't__ take._____

# Jar Of Hearts

**Words & Music by Christina Perri, Drew Lawrence**
**& Barrett Yeretsian**

This bittersweet song about a serial heartbreaker that Perri once dated became a hit in the US after it was featured on the TV show So You Think You Can Dance, and then on Glee. It spent 22 weeks in the UK charts, peaking at No. 4, and in November 2011 she performed it on the BBC's Strictly Come Dancing results show.

**Hints & Tips:** Experiment with dynamics in this song- try playing the opening verse *piano* and the chorus (from bar 13) *forte*. Watch out for accidental passage in the left hand, starting from bar 22.

# Lightning

**Words & Music by Wayne Hector, Steve Mac & Ed Drewett**

Formed in 2009 after a mass audition, this British and Irish boy band released their second album *Battleground* in November 2011. This was the third single taken from it and reached No. 2 in the UK charts, Lightning being explained by one band member as a metaphor to describe the nerves and excitement as you kiss someone.

**Hints & Tips:** Make sure you don't hold the crotchets for too long in bars 5 – 8 and 13 – 16; sometimes the rests are just as important to the sound of a piece as the notes are.

_17_ **F**

touch mine ___ it's the kiss ___ of life. ___ I know, ___

_21_ **B♭**

___ I know that it's a lit - tle bit fright - 'ning. We might as well be

_24_ **F**

play-ing with light - ning. We touch live ___ like it's our ___ first time.

_28_ **B♭**

___ Oh, oh. ___ I know that it's a lit - tle bit fright - 'ning.

_31_ **Am** **B♭** **F**

We might as well be play-ing with light- ning, now. ___ Oh, oh.

**21**

# Nothing's Real But Love

### Words & Music by Francis White & Rebecca Ferguson

After a succession of failed auditions and broken dreams this artist came to prominence in the 2010 version of The X Factor, in which she eventually finished as runner-up. This emotional ballad, her debut single, is about the fickle side of fame and how, amidst the obstacles of every day existence, love is the only thing that matters.

**Hints & Tips:** Practise this carefully, making sure the notes of the chords sound exactly together, especially in bars 23 – 26.

# Marry The Night

**Words & Music by Fernando Garibay & Stefani Germanotta**

The fifth single from her second album *Born This Way* after being recorded on her tour bus, this song is an homage to New York, Lady Gaga's hometown, the lyrics being about her love of partying through the night and committing oneself wholeheartedly to what you're most passionate about which, in her case, is music.

**Hints & Tips:** Triplets are a big feature in this song; make sure you get them nice and even. The steady crotchet accompaniment from bar 31 to the end should help you with counting the off-beat rhythm in the melody.

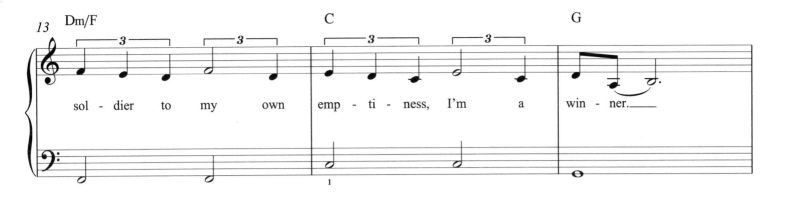

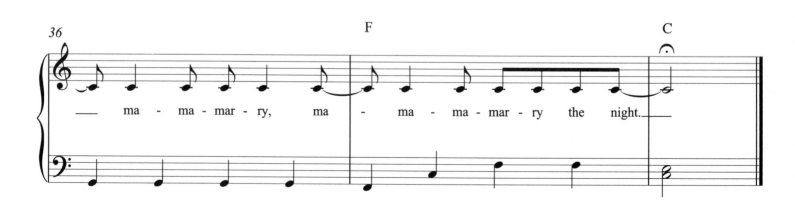

# Moves Like Jagger

**Words & Music by Adam Levine, Benjamin Levin,
Shellback & Ammar Malik**

After topping the US Billboard Hot 100, this single went on to sell more than a million copies in the UK, finishing up as the second biggest seller of 2011 despite never topping the charts. Peaking at No. 2 for seven consecutive weeks, in the first six it was uniquely held off the top by six different singles, each debuting directly ahead of it!

**Hints & Tips:** Look through the melody before playing and note where the leaps and tricky spots are in the right hand, so your hand is in the correct position.

Moderately, strong beat ♩ = 128

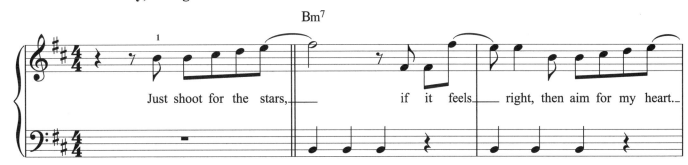

Just shoot for the stars, if it feels right, then aim for my heart.

If you feel like it take me a-way

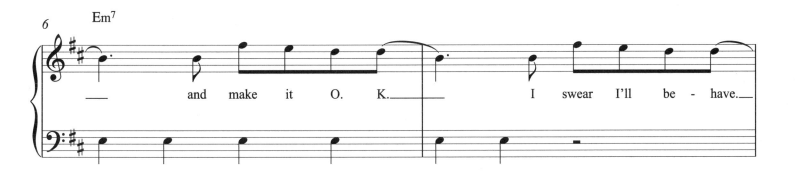

and make it O. K. I swear I'll be-have.

You want-ed con-trol

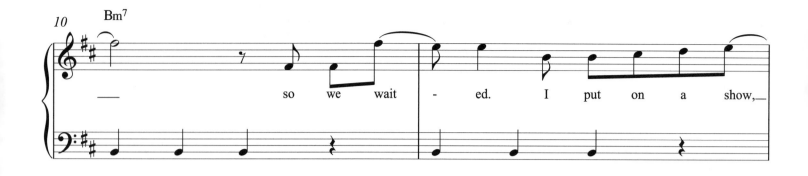

_so we wait - ed. I put on a show,_

_now I'm nak - ed. You say I'm a kid,_

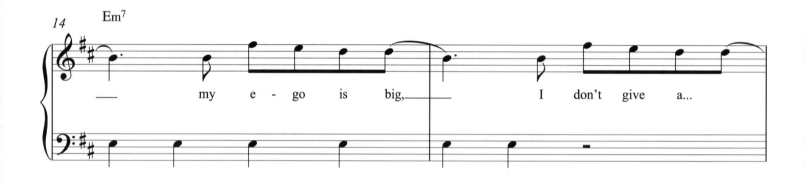

_my e - go is big, I don't give a..._

_And it goes like this._

_Take me by the tongue and I'll know you._ _Kiss me till you're drunk_

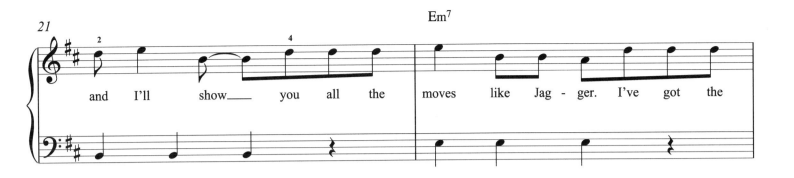

**21**

and I'll show___ you all the moves like Jag - ger. I've got the

**23**

moves like Jag - ger. I've got the moves___ like Jag - ger.___

**26** Bm

I don't need to try to con - trol___ you. Look in - to my eyes

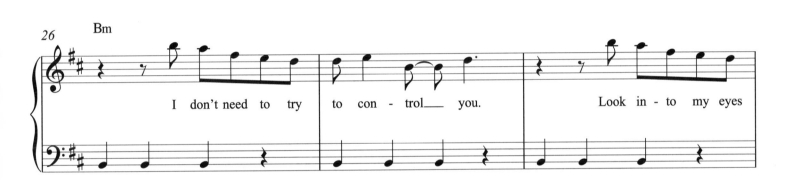

**29**

and I'll own___ you with the moves like Jag - ger. I've got the

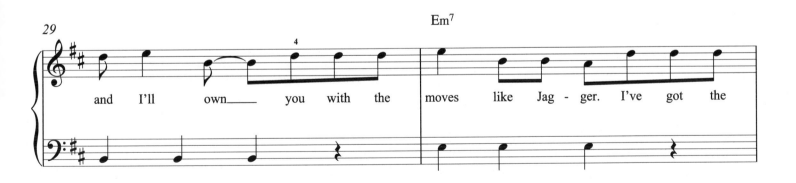

**31**

moves like Jag - ger. I've got the moves___ like Jag___ ger.

# The One That Got Away

**Words & Music by Lukasz Gottwald, Katy Perry & Martin Max**

The chart success of this mid-tempo ballad, a bittersweet story about a lost love, helped Katy Perry become the first female artist to have five hits on the Billboard Hot 100 in one year and the first artist to spend 52 consecutive weeks in its top 10. No surprise then that she was elected MTV's 2011 Artist of the Year.

**Hints & Tips:** The rhythm is mostly steady and straightforward, but have a look at the right hand in bar 16 – this is a bit trickier and crops up a few times, so make sure you've got the hang of it before tackling the whole piece.

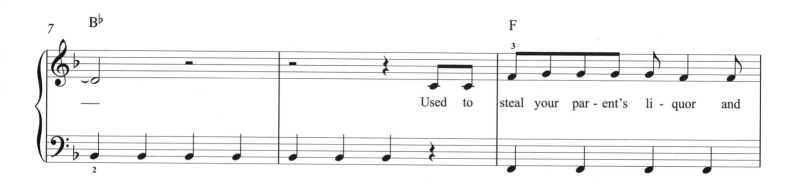

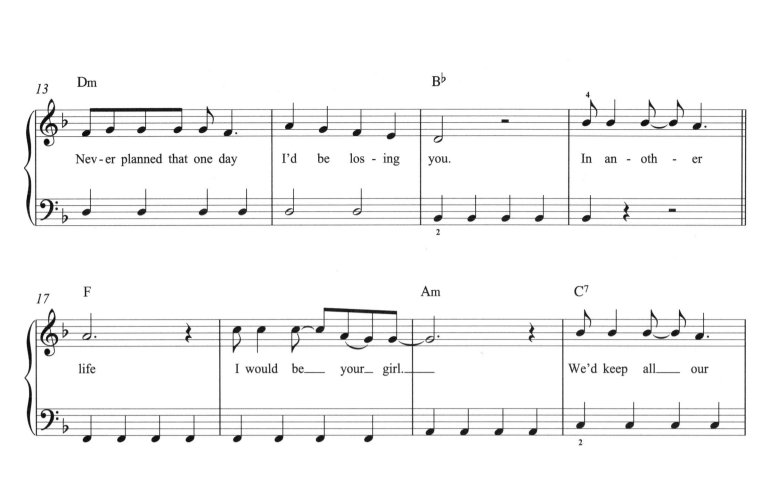

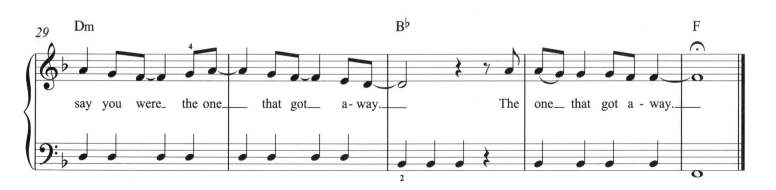

# Our Day Will Come

**Words by Mort Garson**
**Music by Bob Hilliard**

After Dionne Warwick recorded the original demo, this song was released in bossa-nova style by Ruby And The Romantics, getting to No. 1 in the US in 1963. Amy's reggae version was recorded for her debut album *Frank* but was shelved, later to be issued as the first single from her posthumous album *Lioness: Hidden Treasures*.

**Hints & Tips:** Check carefully though this song for accidentals, as there are quite a few throughout.

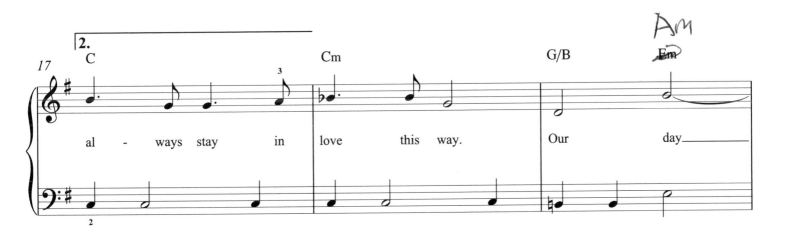

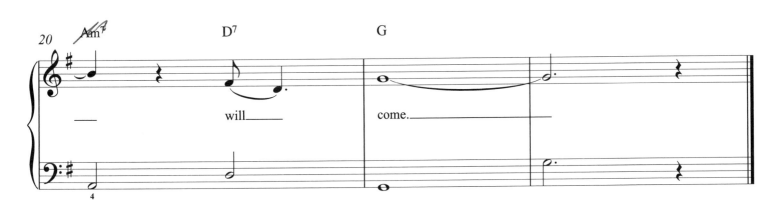

# Paradise

**Words & Music by Chris Martin, Guy Berryman, Jon Buckland,
Will Champion & Brian Eno**

This song about a young girl's dashed hopes and dreams became the UK's first No. 1 single of 2012 and only
the band's second, no less than 16 weeks after its initial release. For the first six it had been ineligible for the
charts, it being available as a free download to those pre-ordering the album *Mylo Xyloto*, on which it appears.

**Hints & Tips:** There are lots of changes of hand position throughout, especially in the first few bars.
Start off playing this slowly and gradually build up the speed.

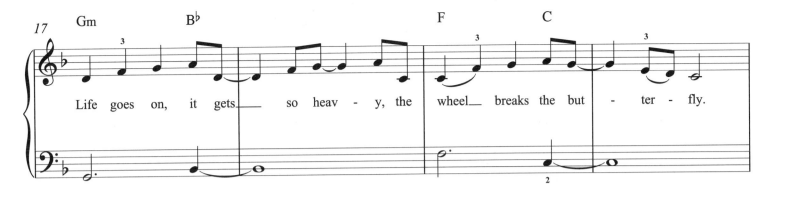

Life goes on, it gets___ so heav- y, the wheel___ breaks the but - ter - fly.

Ev -'ry tear, a wa - ter- fall.___ In the night, the storm-y night,___ she'll close her___

eyes.___ In the night, the storm- y night,___

*D.S. al Fine*

___ a - way she'd___ fly.___ And dream of

# Skinny Love

**Words & Music by Justin Vernon**

At the age of 12 Birdy won both the Under-18s section and the Grand Prize of the talent competition Open Mic UK, performing one of her own compositions. Recorded when she was 14 and released as her debut single in January 2011, this is a cover of a song that the American indie folk band Bon Iver released in the UK in 2008.

**Hints & Tips:** This is a soft and gentle song and should be played *mezzo piano*. Count through the right hand rhythms carefully; use the steady minims in the left hand to help keep time.

Tell my love___ to wreck___ it all.

Cut out all the ropes___ and let me fall.___ My my my,___

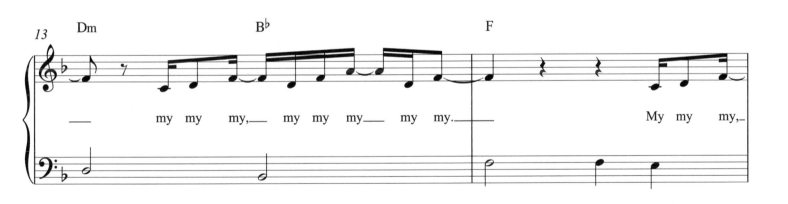

___ my my my,___ my my my___ my my.___ My my my,___

___ my my my,___ my my my___ my my.

# Set Fire To The Rain

## Words & Music by Fraser Smith & Adele Adkins

The third single released from the album *21*, this song, about the contradictions that complicate relationships, reached No. 11 in the UK. It was co-written with Fraser Smith, one of several songwriters Adele collaborated with for the first time on *21*.

**Hints & Tips:** Practise the left hand quaver patterns thoroughly. Go over the right hand chords in bars 22 and 24, making sure the notes sound together.

# Video Games

**Words & Music by Elizabeth Grant & Justin Parker**

This song about the frustration of making all the running in a relationship with an ex-boyfriend is Del Ray's debut single, recorded with lower vocals in the hope of her being seen as a serious artist. She adopted her stage name after management advice that one reminiscent of Hollywood glamour would better suit her kind of music.

**Hints & Tips:** Note the tempo; it's quite slow, so take you're time but try not to let it drag.

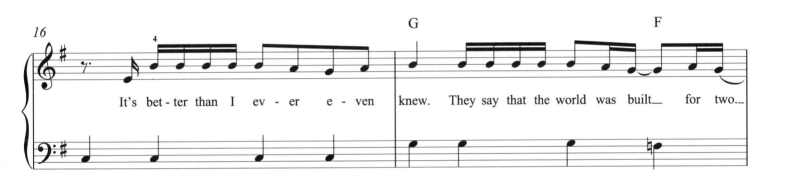

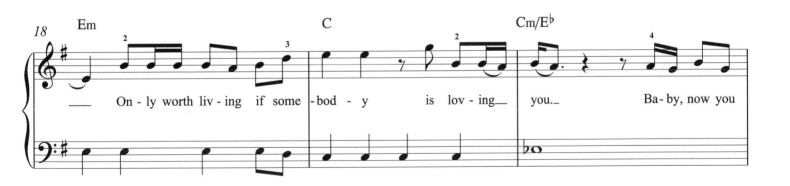

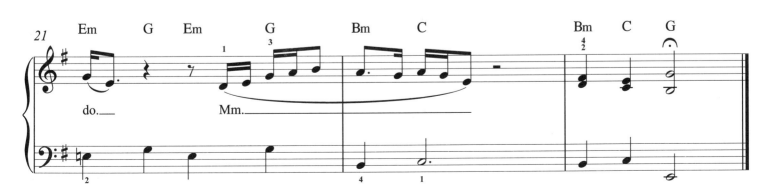

# We Found Love

**Words & Music by Calvin Harris**

In 2011 Rihanna spent more time at the top of the UK Singles charts than any other artist, this song being her sixth No. 1 spread over five consecutive years, a record unequalled by any other female solo artist. It was also her 11th No. 1 on the US Billboard Hot 100, making her the quickest solo artist to amass twenty Top 10 singles.

**Hints & Tips:** The melody is very repetitive, so be as expressive as you can or it could sound dull.

- ny,_____ but I've got-ta let___ it go.___

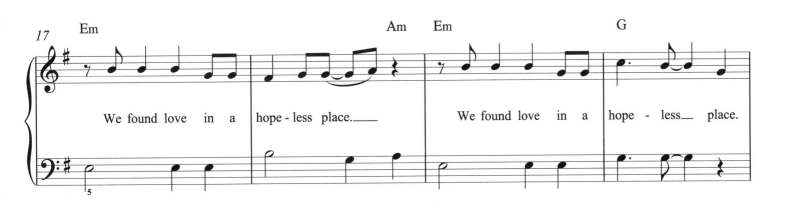

We found love in a hope-less place.___ We found love in a hope-less___ place.

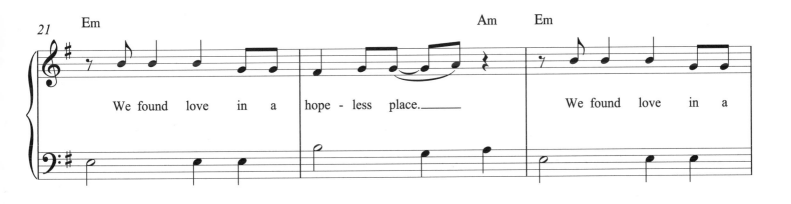

We found love in a hope-less place.___ We found love in a

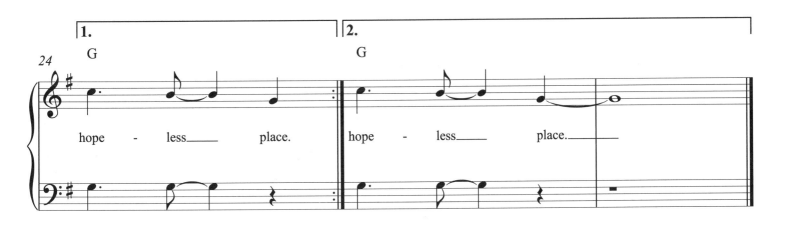

1.

hope - less___ place.

2.

hope - less___ place.___

# Who You Are

**Words & Music by Shelly Peiken, Tobias Gad
& Jessica Cornish**

Written after a lonely three-month trip to Los Angeles when she was shunted from studio to studio, Jessie J credits this song for having saved her life musically. Released in the UK as the fifth single from her debut album of the same name, it spent a total of 11 weeks in the charts, peaking at No. 8.

**Hints & Tips:** Don't start this song too slowly; use the steady, driving rhythm in the left hand to help keep time. Look out for the sudden change of hand position in bar 24 and have the right hand fourth finger ready.

Moderately, strong beat ♩ = 130

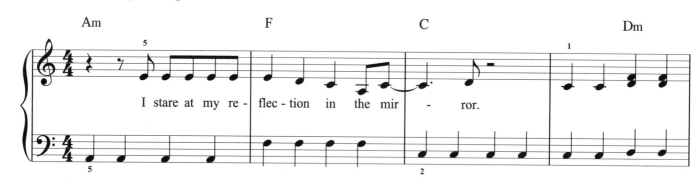

I stare at my re- flec - tion in the mir - ror.

Why am I do - ing this to my - self?

Los- ing my mind on a ti - ny er - ror.

I near-ly left the real me on the shelf. No, no, no, no, no.

# Wherever You Will Go

**Words & Music by Aaron Kamin & Alex Band**

The most successful hit by American alternative rock band The Calling when they released it in 2001, ten years later this version by Brit School graduate Charlene Soraia became popular in the UK, spending 13 weeks in the charts and peaking at No. 3 after it was used in an advert for Twinings tea and also featured on The X Factor.

**Hints & Tips:** This song should be kept nice and light. Make sure the wrist of your left hand isn't too rigid, and use a 'rolling' motion for arpeggio style accompaniment starting in bar 9 if you're finding the stretch too big.